# If I Was Born in...

By Sachiko Otohata

This book belongs to: _____

With love from: _____

In every country wind blows
In every country flowers bloom

But beauty is always different
Beauty is always our own

If I was born in Lyon, France
I would walk with a quick step on the cobblestone

Carrying a novel under my arm
Dreaming of becoming an artist

If I was born in Ulaanbaatar, Mongolia
I would ride through a field on a galloping, wild horse

Leaving any worries far behind
Pushing my dreams forward through the crisp air

If I was born in Tahiti, French Polynesia
I would stroll on a white sand beach

Listening to the endless waves exploring the world
My toes wrapped in their gentle memory

If I was born in Warsaw, Poland
I would walk on a deep snowy road

Watching my frosty breath dance in the cold air
My grandmother's warm stew waits for me at home

If I was born in Toronto, Canada
I would watch the world come together
from my high condo window

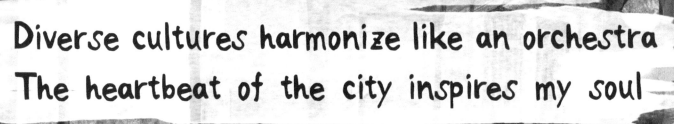

Diverse cultures harmonize like an orchestra
The heartbeat of the city inspires my soul

If I was born in Juba, South Sudan
I would walk to get fresh water for my family

Holding the hand of my strong little brother
Playing with our shadows cast upon the dusty road

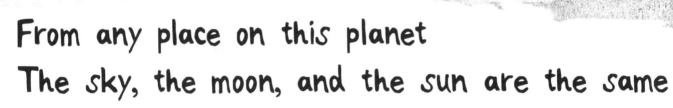

From any place on this planet
The sky, the moon, and the sun are the same

But beauty is always different
Beauty is always our own

And the world is there to have someone very special like you to discover its beauty

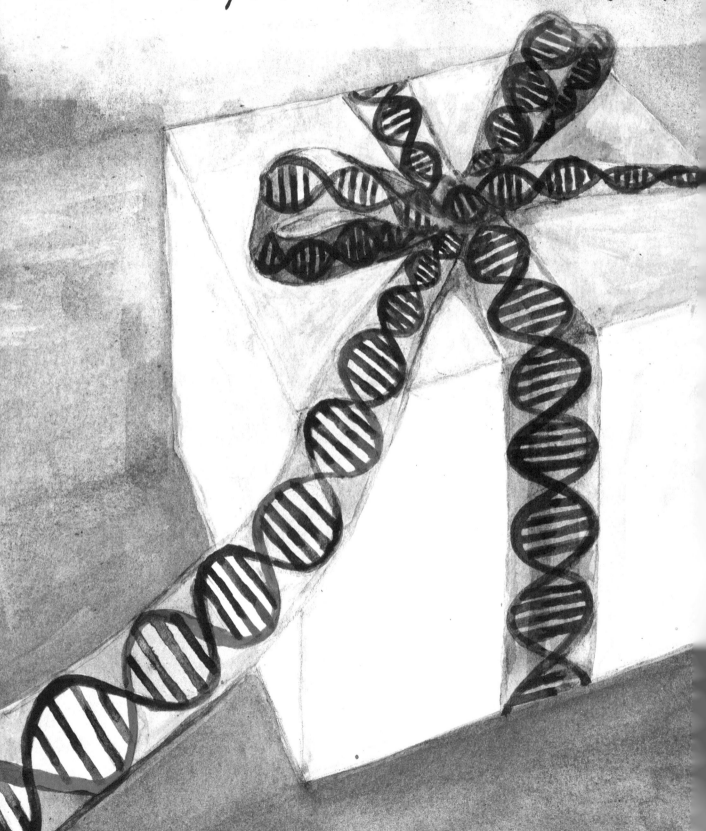

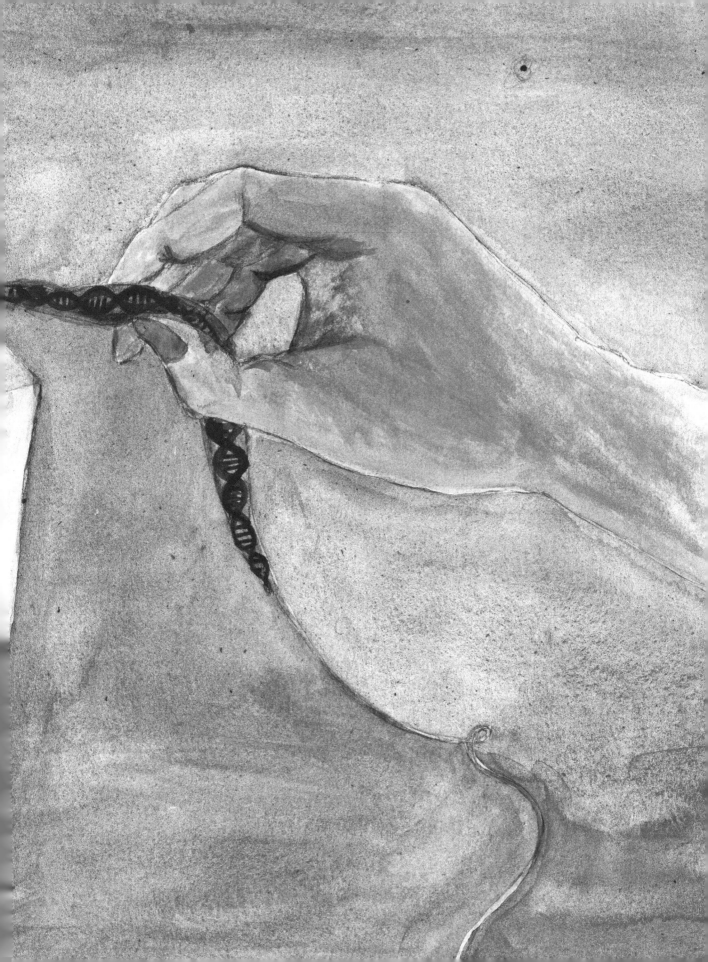

Special thanks to all my friends
who inspired me and helped me create this book,
and to my husband, Brendyn, who always supports me.

- Sachiko (Author/Illustrator)

Sachiko Otohata - Author/Illustrator

🌐 factorysachi.com
📷 factorysachi (Instagram/Facebook)